microbursts

text by Elizabeth Reeder

the structure of the collection is a collaboration
between Reeder and Thomson

images, artwork and original format
by Amanda Thomson

Elizabeth Reeder, originally from Chicago, now lives in Scotland. She writes fiction, narrative non-fiction and hybrid work that creates spaces between forms, subjects and disciplines. Her work explores identity, family, illness and grief, creativity and landscapes. She has published two previous novels, *Ramshackle* and *Fremont*, and her latest novel, *An Archive of Happiness*, was published by Penned in the Margins in September 2020. She is a MacDowell Fellow and a senior lecturer in Creative Writing at University of Glasgow. Her website is: elizabethkreeder.com

Amanda Thomson is a visual artist and writer who is also a lecturer at the Glasgow School of Art. Her interdisciplinary practice is often about notions of home, movements, migrations, landscapes and the natural world and how places come to be made, and she has exhibited nationally and internationally. She earned her doctorate in interdisciplinary arts practice, based around the landscapes and the forests of the North of Scotland, in 2013. She lives and works in Glasgow and in Strathspey. Her first book, *A Scots Dictionary of Nature*, is published by Saraband Books. Her website is: www.passingplace.com

Italicized sections of text are taken from other original sources, which are detailed in Notes and Influences *at the end.*

*It is sheer good fortune to
miss somebody before they leave you.*
(Toni Morrison)

between places

There are words for the kinds of spaces that exist between other places and many of them are about landscape like littoral, ecotone, twilight. In between places there is something solid, a traveler, crossing over. The very details noticed in the midst of travel or shock or bewilderment can hold us fast; lost becomes found, the strange settles into a familiar. In the Black Cuillin of Skye, northwest of where I live, a compass will not work because the magnetic hills disrupt the heart of this simple object that gives direction.

In February 2010, I take notes even when I'm too tired. With my computer on my lap I video a note of each day. My hair is up or down, glasses on or perched, and my eyes are sleep-filled. The last recording, just past midnight and into the nineteenth, is grainy, like an old film, filmed in the dark of his room. The small light on top of the bureau is not up to the job of illuminating. I whisper and sometimes in the background dad can be heard. This is all I will write of this night: how we listen.

On 16 October 2013, the conversation with my mom lasts only three minutes. By evening she's unable to speak and the meds they give her over the next few days are quickly noted and point only towards one thing. Here in these places between lost and found I witness in silence and in deafening chaos and I make up stories that will be memories. Walking upon terra incognita love becomes grief and essay, poem. Each memory forges a new path and this writing acts like a magnet pressed to the face of my compass.

one

year

what we did not know

On some hills, where rocks balance on inclines, there is a point geologists call the angle of no strain. Rocks repose despite steepness because all conditions allow for rest. I sleep lying down, pace upright, and when I lean I need a wall or a chair or a person to lean against.

During this first summer we dismantle a home and forget how to talk to each other. We nearly break up, more than once, and then it's autumn and we move from Scotland to Chicago carrying four items of luggage, which we hope will last the two years we'll spend there.

Our new apartment is filthy, noisy and perfectly located for you to travel south and for me to travel north. Your train loops the Loop; mine goes to the end of the line and returns. We're a closed system and there's pressure from inside, and out, to break apart our vicious little circle.

lost wax casting

A wricht builds coffins and cabinets and all sorts of things out of wood and often needs other objects to complete the task: lock and key, hinge, clasp; something to line the inside of the box. Seamstress wordsmith wricht. A tree becomes a boat or a door; an old joist becomes a chair or something to place across the road for traction when the rains come on. In New Mexico, Walter De Maria forged lightning rods, needlesharp to seduce light and fire to the ground, and under his wooden table I place a single hand on your thigh and later there's a catching of hands as we walk through a lightning field with distant peaks creating and withholding stormclouds. Still later, here, our wedding band is plain, is what is turned and pressed and worried when in crisis, when in doubt, and home can be a foundry for if the band is lost or sold or melted down we are still left with the bond between us.

Genesis is a key pressed into butter, wax, something impressionable. It is clear like the bright call of waxwings as they trill from berry to branch in a clutch of days that can never be predicted. The beginning and the remembered. Remove it, cast it, palm it. Wait for the opportunity to put the key to use, and then pay attention as one surface communicates with another.

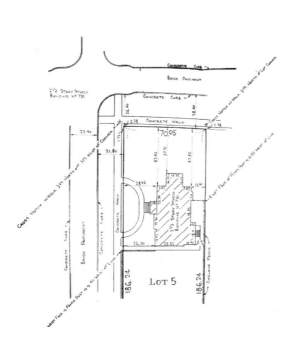

ghosts

On the edge of the lake sits a house, half built in depression, half in wealth. With the help of friends her dad raised it from the ground, with his bare hands, in hard times. But that was years ago and now it's the neighborhood eyesore on such a sought after piece of land beside the water. Storm surges beat at her door as her husband locks cupboards and opens drawers, inappropriately. Just before it's razed, I stand on the potholed driveway and can see right through the place, past closed drawers and open cupboards and out to the water. Two blocks away, at seven thirty-one, my mom is dizzy and my dad says he's doing fine but he often says, Honey could you just run and get this for me. This afternoon they've got what they need; I'm on my way home to our apartment and from the L tracks I see lakescapes and skyscrapers and flags flying at Wrigley Field and when I was fifteen my dad nearly died, the lake rose, and retreated, he came back and the lake the lake the lake in all seasons.

witness, dual national

This paper is the size of a truck and used to be a tree. It lies between us, on the floor, and used to be a mulberry growing near here. We sat in its shade, kissed, picked up a leaf, and this found object made it into your art, my writing.

Paper made like this, wisp thin, treelines still visible, is art. And the lifelines of it are pretty: like lips, hips, skin. It's like the place on your back where I touch the shadow cast by your vertebrae after we've made love. You don't let me do this often and today your body is held tight and your eyes are dark and unbound. Our thoughts are brutal, battlescarred, and you've almost had enough of it all. But you're not talking, haven't been talking for a long time. It's your closed hand that gives you away: skeleton bones and thick knuckles, pale broken by red. You don't even know you're upset; I am witness and so live it for you.

There's what's left of a dead tree between us: cut, pulped, reformed. You hold a charcoal in your hand and I have a thin-nibbed pen in mine. Our bodies are connected over this space by invisible threads of fear; I squat, my feet holding down the bark-remnant. You stretch out on your belly, your now open palm splayed on the page like an embossment. Like earth over a new grave. We've never been this close to the end before. If we can laugh it will be okay. A bell rings, echoes through the next minutes. You start in one corner, me another, and we may meet in the middle or you might fly off one edge and me the other.

timescale unknown, as a daughter

You limp and pause. It looks like your hips are sore, like the sockets are too wide to hold your weight. You never talk about your hips. Or your congested heart which struggles, lets water gather in your lungs, your legs. While you are physically heavy, your spirit is light, held aloft, high like your breaths. I can't quite feel that you're here on earth; on some days you're away, simply split between places, between here and somewhere else. Somewhere dead. And then you come back, laughing, eating donuts and drinking coffee, finishing the crossword in a flash, yelling at the sports on the tv, and you're all you dad and you're never going to die.

You shuffle your tall thin frame; you can't quite always lift your feet. They are too heavy, so is your head, and it leads you when you walk. We can't talk about your heart, it's weary, terrified, does it have to keep beating? If it stops, you don't want it started again. It flutters like your hands, trembles to flight. But your heart will keep beating because there is nothing wrong with it besides a little calcification, normal for a woman your age.

legend

Some Native Americans look in six
directions to locate themselves (add
sky, earth) and then they look in.
The body a hold*fast*. Others describe
the landscape in relation to their
bodies, where something stands in
relation to where they're facing: I see
from here, they say, and I look out;
I tell you what I see.

legend

Some Native Americans look in six
directions to locate themselves (add
sky, earth) and then they look in.
The body a *holdfast*. Others describe
the landscape in relation to their
bodies, where something stands in
relation to where they're facing: I see
from here, they say, and I look out;
I tell you what I see.

buildings define the space
of the street

My dad nearly died when he was
forty-nine: heart attack and triple
bypass; blood clots in his legs;
another heart attack. Halloween,
Christmas, New Year, Valentine's
Day. The bypass graft didn't stick
and he was given no more than five
years to live.

Two decades later and he's
not walking very well, my mom is
dizzy nearly all the time, and I've
moved back to my home town and
am drinking coffee and watching a
peregrine split a halo of pigeons wide
open. The bird makes daring dives
between the buildings of Ashland
Avenue, the speckled lines of her tail
sleek in front of the bright sky. She's
honing in on the dirty grey spread
of pigeons, the predator's eyes on a
slow one, and there she goes, a fast
slice down and to the side and up
and out of sight.

Those pigeons live on top of
the car park and I watch; they don't
settle for ages. They fly around and
around, looking more like starlings,
those smaller dark mice with wings.
On the wing. On the wing when their
cluster has been split open.

the buzz

A hummingbird feeds on my mom's
hot-pink jerusalem roses in the early
sun, thick heat, and it's almost still
at the bud. The mesmerizing buzz of
wings, the bright exposed neck. Days
pass and cool and with a broom an old
woman shakes an apple from a tree
across the way, bites in, and music
falls through a floor, into a ceiling,
into my room, *and my memories
– those elusive, fragmentary patches of
color and feeling – are gone; they've
been replaced by the work.*

a door is a door is a door

is   an entrance
          an exit
          a portal
          an heirloom
          an excuse
          it's a reason to go
          and to stay, stay

subterranean, northshore

The sand hot between our toes we
walk and cool evening blows across
the top layer of sand as a man with
an alcoholic's nose runs one-way
along the water's edge and swims
home. From his porch an angry
homeowner hits golf balls at us, as if
he could own the harvest moon. We
find them and chuck them into the
water; we bury them deep.

as we migrate

There's this bird lady and she saves
birds, you know, the ones that fly
into high buildings as they migrate.
The highest skyscrapers turn off
their lights for three weeks during
the autumn migration and for some
lights-off is not enough because
there's still clear glass and seductive
atrium trees.

With a butterfly net in hand,
at dawn, she trawls the base of
buildings, traps dazed birds and puts
them into paper lunch bags. Wild dry
flutter-rustle in bursts like someone
drowning coming up for air

—
—
—
—
—
—

Hours later, still that sound. Until she packs them away, closes the trunk of her car, looks up and then at me. What an ugly building, she says.

Walking home, and for days and weeks after, still today, I look up, see their proud sleek lines, that tall seductive glass. Some are in awe as they fly past.

lsd

He's in the ICU and I didn't ask
enough questions. Six hours later,
sleeping at my parents' house, I feel
inadequate. I'm not sure I did enough
for dad: I brought the wrong mask
for his breathing machine, didn't
even bring the right attachment.
Could do better. This is mine to bear
and I don't want to sleep on a single
mattress with you, instead I sleep
alone downstairs on the couch.

The next day I drive back along
lake shore drive to the apartment to
pick up some clothes, a toothbrush.
The lake churns up algae green and
concrete grey, the waves coming in
from the northeast, and the wind
explains why I was so cold last night.
A winter lake, pre-freeze, all the boats
in the harbor gone, small stubs of
piers. And space. Winter gives vistas.
Bare branches, spindly into the ice-
blue sky; the sun so clearly defining
what is here and what is absent.

thanksgiving

My brother and sister and their families arrive at our parents' house. I've been here since last Friday, when he went into the ICU. Dad has been in some form of congestive heart failure for nearly twenty years and he'd been sleeping for hours on end in an upright wooden chair, in the breakfast room because he couldn't make it up the stairs.

It's Thanksgiving Thursday and this house now holds ten adults, two walking talking kids, a newborn, and two dogs. This house used to feel huge and now feels barely big enough to hold us all. In fact, there aren't enough beds, and my sister offers to stay in a hotel. On his first day home, my dad is still falling asleep everywhere, can't remember simple facts of the last week; I keep checking him while he sleeps to make sure he's still breathing. And yet my sister wants to leave her kids in the house with all of us while she and her husband stay at a hotel. We drop hints, try to get her to realize we don't have the time and energy to look after her kids, but in the end my sister has to be asked to take her son, at least, with her.

the healthy one

Dad is still slurring his words, so out of it that he doesn't take any of his meds on his first night home from the hospital, his skin hanging off him, and yet he's still puffy, his memory affected, his breath, halted, cut off. His short gait, uneven, and I can see the straight pain shoot through the roundness of his hip joints. His legs, which he insists aren't retaining water, are, nonetheless, hardly bending at all on his way up the stairs. His left leg goes first. His right follows. Six half, halted breaths per step, not like he's been asked to do it – in through the nose out through pursed lips to give him more oxygen – and I'm worried about him by the third step. Worried because he's too heavy for me to stop if he staggers backwards, or if he stalls. Seven more stairs to go. And then five. And then a dozen flat shuffled steps to the folding chair unfolded in front of his bed. His stride is shorter than it used to be. In two months time, after my mom's had surgery, when she can't move her head on the bed, or when her hands shake so much she can't put on her glasses, or hold a cup of water steady enough to drink, he'll say he's the healthy one.

Lost really has two disparate meanings. Losing things is about the familiar falling away, getting lost is about the unfamiliar appearing... Either way there is a loss of control. Imagine yourself streaming through time shedding gloves, umbrellas, wrenches, books, friends, homes, names. This is what the view looks like if you take a rear-facing seat on the train. Looking forward you constantly acquire moments of arrival, moments of realization, moments of discovery.

Dad is not well. He sleeps for a full twenty-four hours. When we try to give him his meds the next day, my brother and I are sure we'll give him the wrong pills, the wrong doses, and with this many pills surely we'll kill him. Dad forces them down with water; refuses food. He won't let my brother help him to the bathroom but my brother sits outside the door for over half an hour to make sure dad's okay. It's possible dad's fallen asleep; it's absolute that he's nauseous with the meds. He makes it back to bed, sleeps more. We help him down the stairs the next day, Friday, for our delayed Thanksgiving dinner. He's a patriarch in name only. He's not feeling any better on Saturday and talks about going to the doctor's open clinic the next day. He's barely walking, can't hold his attention long enough to carry on a brief conversation, and we say we think it's unsafe for him to drive. My brother and I, separately, more than once, offer to take him the next morning. He wakes up before seven on Sunday and asks my sister-in-law to move their car so he can get his car out. She does.

What should I have said? she says comforting her newborn after she's rushed upstairs to tell us, I didn't know how to say no.

Dad's already gone. He could kill someone, kill himself, and he's made my sister-in-law complicit in anything that might happen.

Excuse me, I say, and go back into the room where you are still in bed. I close the door, Pack up our stuff. If they don't fucking want my help then I'll not fucking give it.

My brother knocks on the door, Let's go get him.

It takes a few phone calls and three phone books to find the right address. We're just over the train tracks sitting at the lights and both of us stare at a tree fluttering with birds; as we drive by and see plain old starlings rustling there I say, I thought those were waxwings.

So did I, he says.

The doctor's office is quiet, we introduce ourselves to the nurse at the desk, who disappears, finds dad and asks if it's okay if we come in. He says yes and she shows us to where my dad sits in a room waiting for a doctor. He's slow and considered speaking to the doctor, it's a long history he has to explain to the newbie, who doesn't say much of anything at all. I'm fine, dad says as we leave, I'm fine. But he lets me drive him home.

28 november

Don't ask me about home. One, many, none. The one we have here is too loud, feels unsafe, is either too hot or too cold, like my life this autumn: without consistency, without moderation. Don't ask my parents about home either. The one they have is inappropriate, and there was an ease with which I went home to my parents' house when my dad was admitted to the ICU. An ease with which I took responsibility for laundry, the house chores, the errands, taking them to doctors' appointments, visiting dad, taking (and forgetting to take, in equal measure) things he needed at the hospital. An ease with which I forgot the apartment. The speed with which you noticed this.

29 november

thundersnow

I sleep while you work on, work and watch tv. When you come to bed you tell me the snow has started, 'although it sounds more like icy rain'. Thick duvet and you strip down for sleep. At five-thirty a noise wakes you, you share it with me and then we drift. The warm air over the water causes it. It's rare.

The next day, you hang out at the apartment; it's your home too, but having you here makes me restless on a weekday. I create a petty gripe and pair it with a real one, magnified, and the anger is right there, sweet, untouched and I could punch a wall.

Last night we had thundersnow, but it didn't accumulate much. Lots of noise, but no follow through: this is me. You are a storm that appears on the horizon after dark falls and the wind picks up the moment sleep takes us, and when we wake in the morning, we're snowed in.

dnr

Next to the power plant today in Morris, Illinois,
was a field superheated in the bitter cold of the day
and the fog of it was thick, chopping off, floating,
trees; the nuclear hot met cold air curling thick as
firesmoke but whiter, white down clouds stirred up
by the ground, by actions requiring warning sirens
that stand like skyscrapers above the flatness of the
fields, sharp boxes to power them and radio stations
listed to tell you what to do, just in case of fallout,
and we parked in front of a sign as we ate sandwiches
and potato chips by the picnic tables but we stayed
in the heated seats of the car because although we're
silly, we're not stupid, and shit it was just too cold
and barren and plus we'd seen three guys in a pickup
truck and even though it said DNR on the side (do
not resuscitate, department of natural resources, do
not resuscitate) and I thought shotgun in the back, or
three, and no one'd be there to witness the murder of
a white girl and a black girl who traveled all the way
to the powerplant's shadow in a borrowed car to see
dead winter prairie and it's there we see a few birds of
prey (bop bop): one thin and long and wide and the
other huskier, bulky with a white breast, and loads
of northern flickers on the ground, and around the
curve of the road it was quiet and through the trees
we could see the truck and the government building
and we stopped and were quiet but we left without
walking and in Scotland I'm not always confident out
in nature but I don't ever worry about getting shot
and buried, sometimes just shot, if it's culling season.

baseball-hail

I'm sorry you couldn't be more
understanding and supportive to
mom, my dad said to my sister in
an email and he cc'd me and my
brother in. If I'm thundersnow after
midnight, my sister's baseball-sized
hail, midday, the day you park your
car on the street.

My mom has surgery to remove a
lump on her lung, which should be
a relatively clean procedure, two days
in the hospital at most, but when she
comes out of surgery she can't move
her head, can't hold a cup of water
or scratch her face or put her glasses
on. She can't move her legs on the
bed either. She's in pain, but not able
to describe it, to do more than moan.
Morphine bugs climb the walls, and
the men who walk on air between the
street lights upset her.

yell

In the middle, I'm quiet. All the talk. I listen, I ask, I don't offer opinions. Enable, offer directions, gentle. I'm quiet. All the talk. All the anger. I think I know. They think they know. I'm efficient. They're being blinded: one by despair, one by hope. That would be fine but it's my life they're messing with too. I'm silent. On the way to my parents' house, the warning light goes on in my mom's car. I meet my dad at the car mechanic's, drive his car to check out the rehab place for my mom (after five days in the hospital, she still can't walk, she's still on oxygen, and can't do the stairs of their house), go back to pick up the car, and I attempt to get back to the hospital. On the expressway, the warning light comes on again. I exit I-94 and make it to 731, hoping dad's home with the other car. He's not. In the garage I roar; I hold nothing back. I stand and yell. I crouch down and I yell and I sob. Like I'm in mourning; what am I mourning? I stand up, go inside, and call the car repair place and say firmly, harshly to the machine: When you say a car is fixed, it should be fixed. My mom is waiting for me at the hospital to be with her as she's transferred and I can't get there. When you say a car is fixed, make sure the car is fixed. My face is salty and red. I pull down my shirt, smooth it; drink water. Hydrate. Hydrate. Stay healthy. My dad comes home, You can't cry, you're our rock. I drive his car to the hospital and I am silent, useful, helpful. I drive back and pick him up, we go out and see mom at rehab. I drive him and me back to their house. That night I hear a loud crash and dad's gone down in his bathroom and has broken his foot. Days later, when I finally get home, I'm rude to my girlfriend.

irreverent

My mom's been shacked up in an old folks' home for three days now. I'm aiming to have her home by Friday but I think I'm the only one. Realistically it'll be the week after. Or the week after that. I drive around in their car because I don't have my own; I'm running errands, doing their laundry, problem-solving with nurses and social workers, and then hanging out with my mom so she knows it's all okay, and making sure she pulls out the stops and gets her butt out of there the minute she can do the fifteen steps of their house, unaided.

She had surgery last week, which actually went well (no cancer) but the recovery has been a mean knee-capping bastard that gives her the shakes. That's her story. Really it's not the surgery but something undiagnosed which had been degenerating before she had part of her lung taken out, and she won't go to the neurologist because she'll tell her something she doesn't want to know, something that would actually mean they have to plan for an ugly future.

So she's in rehab, 'because of surgery', and I'm just back from visiting her, the two-hour drive home, and she's on the phone, complaining about my dad.

I never wanted to be

an old man who fell down all the time

It's a flail. Involuntary. The wild twitch which cuts a line out of forced stillness, the slurred steps of a shifted gait. This arm here, struck out. Imagine a light held by two pinched fingers (if they could still pinch), lights off, slow shutter speed, and it arcs, a yoyo caught in light, in flight. It's not like she doesn't know, she does.

This man in the wheelchair, a c-curve of a back, his face expressionless, something else that goes. You can already see it, how mom stares a little bit too long, how her face waits

1

2

3

before curving into a smile. But she knows it and her ears, with turtles dangling (the only earrings she has here) turn red. She looks, slowly, He has Parkinson's, she says.

She blinks, hiding her blue eyes just for a second. And when she walks she lifts her legs clearly until the tenth or eleventh step when her left leg gets tired and doesn't quite clear the floor. I ignore it and she tries to.

my heart is not still

Tonight standing at the front of the
room to teach, I imagine your body
along the front of my own. Thighs
right here, your hand beneath my
shirt, still and cool with a small
chop of water where an icicle has
melted. Standing here I don't say
anything about my mother or her
stay in rehab or about being up at
five a.m., again, or how I cried all
through yesterday. I am silent about
the bitter walks to the frozen lake.
I say nothing about how today at
lunch, sitting across from my dad
in a ubiquitous sandwich place, we
said nothing about how bad mom
looked yesterday, nothing about
how we didn't talk as we stared out
the window at the dirt grey sky or
as we drove in silence to visit her.

In June my dad keeps falling asleep and has started to slur his words. We spot it early enough and get him to the hospital without an ambulance. From a full-to-bursting waiting room, he's triaged second because his heart rate is thirty-seven. The nurse says, If that was me, I'd be crawling, and adds, under her breath, Or out cold. After a brief check-in in the ER, he's back in CCC (cardiac comprehensive care) for five days. They flush his kidneys and send him home.

His June hospitalization had led to some talks of a move, an attempt to find a new place to live; his August hospitalization turns these talks into action. They put money down for a move to a retirement community.

Dad doesn't want to move but the pain in his hips, his knees, his legs, his lungs will not allow him to do what he wants to do, which is to stay and die in the house, as he looks out over his forty acres. He feels the inappropriateness of the house, how he's been stuck on one floor or another for months and mom and I need to run between all floors to get him basic things. Whatever he wants seems to be on a different floor. It frustrates him not to be independent. No amount of planning, no system we come up with can make this house work for him. After they decide to sell the house (in conversations I'm not privy to), mom cries, not only because it's hard to leave a house you've lived in for thirty-two years but mostly because she's stopped taking her meds. Of course she has.

unmapped

Our Glasgow flat is without tenants
for the second month; I spend
most of my time up at my parents'
house; the start of my book is ten
months late, and my parents tell
people I've come here to write.

we're a closed system

The Great Salt Lake cannot be mapped
with any degree of accuracy, because it lies in
a shallow basin without drainage: any slight
change in water level becomes an extensive
change in shoreline.

This is to say I don't know. And I do. I am lost. I know
how to be right here, as a daughter. I know this. And
again and again I don't know what to do in the minute,
to move us out of that minute and successfully into
the next one.

circling the drain

On *The Daily Show*, Ted Koppel was talking about attitudes to terminal illness and death and told this anecdote:

How you doing? Ted asked his ninety-three-year-old neighbor as they both retrieved their morning papers from their front sidewalks.

I'm circling the drain, Ted. I'm circling the drain. His neighbor paused, paper in hand, Remember, Ted, ain't none of us getting out of here alive.

what we did not know

These parables say that representation is always partial, else it would not be representation, but some kind of haunting double. But the terra incognita spaces on maps say that knowledge also is an island surrounded by oceans of the unknown. They signify that the cartographers knew they did not know, and awareness of ignorance is not just ignorance; it's awareness of knowledge's limits.

never let truth get in the way of a good story
(Dad, July 2008; and, I suppose, Mark Twain said it first)

composite and conjecture

John C Fremont was a reckless, cavalier and inconsistent traveler. An amateur at almost everything he did, in the 1840s and 50s, he named plants and places (mostly after himself), he put his men's lives at risk as they traveled west across a still wild and already peopled land colonized by the burgeoning United States via the Louisiana Purchase, and he was convicted of mutiny and military misconduct (after which he ran for the presidency). His wife penned most of his autobiographic journals, journals with names like *The Life of Colonel John Charles Fremont and His Narratives of Explorations and Adventures*.

Decades before him, Lewis and Clark were meticulous. Under Thomas Jefferson's orders in 1803, they traveled west of the Mississippi and out to the Pacific Coast. Traveling by river and on foot and horseback, they observed and measured unfamiliar land and water and landscapes that were already familiar to many. They could not see beyond their own field of vision and when they returned east, Lewis and Clark merged their maps with those of other explorers and cartographers; they mapped what they knew and beyond what had been seen and recorded, they sketched a composited terra incognita, a conjecture.

Maps abstract places and ideas. Give us symbols. Inscribe and challenge bias. We unroll them and hang them on a wall; folded, we carry them with us, and without a compass (a lighthouse, a star) we may still not know enough to save ourselves.

partial source, the mississippi
is thin, so thin in minnesota

The view here is truly magnificent; but, indeed, it needs something to repay the long prairie journey of a thousand miles. The sun has just shot above the wall, and makes a magical change. The whole valley is glowing and bright, and all the mountain peaks are gleaming like silver... And at our evening halt on the Sweet Water the roasted ribs again made their appearance around the fires, and with them, good humor, and laughter, and song were restored to the camp. Our coffee had been expended, but we now made a kind of tea from the roots of the wild cherry tree.

composite and conjecture

After two hours of Chicago-heavy traffic, and two more of vast Illinois flatlands, we hit the brief undulating land at the state border and then cross the Mississippi River at seventy miles per hour in blazing sun. You could blink and be past it. On the prairie of Iowa, lines of pylons cut against blue, the twisted wires white and then blank as we speed by. We drive straight west, hit Des Moines, and wave in the direction of my brother who lives an hour to the north and who we really should stop and see but we're on our way out and so we turn south, driving further into July.

We start the trip all abuzz. Big talks, although I don't remember about what. We're expanding, moving west, we don't have a border, not even a baseline. Through Kansas, Colorado. The air gets drier; the car an instant oven. We're getting bigger, accumulating. We move out, further towards. Further towards what we don't know. There's an edge to going out, especially heading west, how everything flattens, rises, opens itself. Hides its folds, its coolness. We're heading out, the heat is stark.

Into Utah, past the Book Cliffs and a copper mine we can't find, and at the edge of Nevada we pivot and rush back past the salt flats where, in some places, you can still see the wagon wheel tracks made by the first pioneers. Ill-fated or blessed, many crossed this way. Back through Colorado we head northeast and into an interminable Nebraska day. We're setting groundwork for the future. The Rockies are distant behind us. Iowa slips away and we're in Chicago traffic; my phone rings, 3682, but I don't answer it. We don't talk. The skyline to the east is darkening as day falls behind us and into a growing storm.

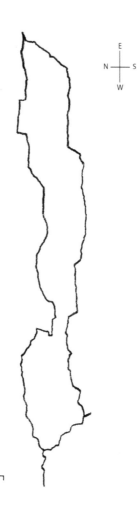

100 mi
200 km

misdirection

At Bingham Canyon Copper Mine, on the outskirts of Salt Lake City, trucks the size of houses transport earth, open-casting, and wide-mouth hoses dampen down fugitive dust. The mine is over one hundred years old, excavated deep and visible from space. I'm fascinated and appalled all at once. Mining copper is a tenacious business, all this earth displaced and here, in the heat of Utah, only the smallest percentage of each scoop of earth is copper, which needs to be extracted. Gold and silver, at even smaller percentages, are happy byproducts. It's about inverting a mountain and transporting all that earth and rock and tailings somewhere else in the state. It's autumn and you take a metal-working class and craft a flat copper compass with *you are here* circling its edges in concentric circles, the needle always finding you found.

terra infirma

Twice she's asked her neurologist
whether she has Parkinson's. Twice
her neurologist has said, Absolutely,
you have Parkinson's. We just have
to assess how it will progress. In
the car, on the way home from
the appointment in which this is
confirmed for the second time, my
mom says, I don't have Parkinson's.
She's wrong. I don't have Parkinson's.
In a few weeks it won't be denial,
she'll have forgotten what Dr K said.
In another month's time, her vision
is faltering again: she's no longer
reading and she's forgotten that a
year ago her optometrist explained
that this sort of difficulty – not being
able to follow a line to the end – is
associated with Parkinson's.

I'm putting all my mom's
symptoms together and thinking the
truth has not yet been fully defined.
terra incognita   terra infirma

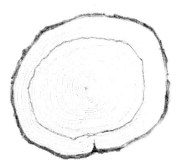

another

year

ghost train

In Graceland Cemetery during the
storm of a century, trees are falling
down and the dark afternoon sky is
lit again and again by lightning, such
August heat. It's in these bursts of
light that the wind shows itself and
the purple line train on this elevated
track rocks back and forth roughly
racing north through these gusts.

GENERAL CHEMISTRY	5		4		3		2		1	
	01/05/08 0658		01/06/08 0805		01/06/08 0807		01/07/08 0612		01/07/08 0621	
GLUCOSE	99				130	▲			114	▲	→ kidney
SODIUM	148	▲			145				145		
POTASSIUM	3.1	▼			3.4	▼			3.2	▼	3.5 is norma
CHLORIDE	109	▲			109	▲			108		
CO2	30				28				25		
BUN	27	▲			29	▲			33	▲	8-23
CREATININE	1.4				1.5	▲			1.6	▲	.6-1.2
CALCIUM	9.4				9.2				9.2		
TOTAL PROTEIN					5.7	▼			5.8	▼	
ALBUMIN					3.3	▼			3.4	▼	
BILIRUBIN TOTAL					1.9	▲			1.9	▲	1.7-1.8
ALK PHOSPHATASE					80				80		
SGOT					21				21		
SGPT					23				24		} liver enzymes
MAGNESIUM	2.1								2.0		
CORTISOL SERUM	26 *										75
AMMONIA	88		68	▲			83	▲			<35

direct 0.4 (normal) → processed through liver

Tuesday ammonia = 64

Tues creatinine 1.4

(48) May 2009
37
INR 1.5

triage

August. Mid-afternoon. My dad can't get out of bed and a storm is upon us. He's hidden a fall from the day before (he's nearly broken his ribs) and his fever rages. This time he can't even get out of bed without the medics. A nurse comes into the ER bay. Sir, she asks as she checks him over, Why do you only have one sock on? She lifts the blanket and exposes his entire right lower leg that is an angry red balloon, with more than one open, yellow, weeping sore. This time it's edema ulcers and septicemia. Just when we thought we knew what to look for, this shows up and we didn't even see the signs. Dad's been hiding symptoms.

In the six days he's there, they don't even bother to try and take the water weight off, or get his kidney numbers to improve, and he's having serious trouble walking. His legs are too big for any of the compression stockings, which means his heart can't pump the liquid out of his legs, which remain in a pitted edema state.

In preparation for putting 731 on the market, mom leads the barrage of cleaning and dumping the house needs; she chooses the realtor and solicits the aid of the faithful Saint Joe: Let Saint Joseph help you sell your property! Just bury his statue, say a prayer and let him go to work for you!

we all deserve a medal

His office is made of paper. Dad sits in his broken office chair that is more electrical tape than metal or cushion and he directs me with his gruff arthritic hands, which lack the finesse that would allow him to do this on his own. We uncover drafts of postcards he wrote while on holiday; the original surveys for 731; three decades of official correspondence. We shred what needs to be shredded, pack up what he'll take with him when they go, and when my sister-in-law visits she says, I didn't know there were shelves in here.

Mom cries about the ice-skating medals I've thrown out as part of the house cleaning; she comes into the room with the black bag, empty, her hands gripping the medals. I ask why she's crying so hard about medals I'd earned when I was nine. She admits she's been off her Lexapro for a while. Then it's November and she cries in the car, at home, and she corners strangers in aisles of supermarkets and cries. I don't want to go this place. I don't want to sell my house.

I watch her shuffle and slow-blink. She frets, but not about the fact that she's unable go down to the basement or do the dishes or open jars or write the checks that need to be written for the upkeep of any house.

fact and fiction

As we empty out 731, the age of the building, the gaps in corners, the possibility of separation, becomes apparent. It's like the Fremont house: belying the state of the family living within it.

15 november

The signs go up in front of the house.

direction is the moment
you choose

In this midst of this we have *jungle fear*. It's
like woods shock, but more overwhelming.

16 november

Mom found dad lying on his bedroom floor. 11:30 am and we have no idea how long he'd been lying there. He didn't respond when she shouted his name. To get into the room she had to force his leg to the side with the door. His c-pap machine blew oxygen out of the mask into the air of the room. She'd already dialed 911 and dad said, Don't call 911. She hung up. They phoned her back, Do you need help? Yes, I think I do. The paramedics came. Forty-five minutes later, when I meet them in the ER, his eyes are thick with yellow mucus and he falls in and out of consciousness. Family is place. This is why we're here. I sit by his bed, hoping he'll recover, and in me I hold another country. A memory of Assynt acts as a corset around my ribs as I try to catch a breath, any breath – the loch with a boat attached to a red buoy on its barely rippled surface, the heather brown hills beyond brought low by thick mist, leafless rowans clinging to the edge of the water. I've been known to cry out there, like I've been known to cry in the Rothko room at the Tate, or in the car with the music blasting as I drive once again to the hospital.

microburst   what you do not remember somehow resides here in this room where you've been taken, your swollen legs are red-angry like a sky in storm at dusk with silver-coated bandages over their weeping and you can feel but can't see the broken horizon-lines that puncture the peaceful coast of your neck and folds of skin hang down and then retreat with the thanksgiving days and with the meds they give you, and your hands are skinny for all that, veins popping over the bones, over the knobs of arthritis or gout (they don't know which), and in sleep you raise your head on the inhale as if to make room in your busy chest for air and your chin falls down when you're empty and the floor is where you were found a few days ago, taken by a fast shock which sent you not to your knees but flat onto your back, your heart so slow, face so swollen that for more than a few seconds she thought you were dead and through the yellow of your eyes you do not always recognize us and mom has to sign the form, we have to trust you'll not die here on the table, and trust that you might die if we don't sign, and the level of doctor-nurse activity says it all, this could be it, this is it   and after three days in ICU they you move to CCC and the shirt you wear over your gown gives you just enough decency to barter with a realtor over the details of the weirdly demanding offer of someone wanting to buy the house you've lived in for thirty-two years and it's home to some, a reluctant sale if it goes through, but stairs are stairs (you want mom to be safe too) and your legs are your legs and now your burning feet aren't even eager to take you someplace slowly and you're not afraid of the point of departure but traveling there is nothing but painful, recalling how you're losing your forty acres   all the blinds up in the house when you and mom usually keep them down and in this autumn night when I look up, my brother beside me, the house ablaze with lights, your den looks Rockwell-esque, like poetry, and the number crunching business of heading a family takes on the timbre and rhythm of elegy, a dirge   the light, the warm light hitting off the wood of your office shelves, the organizational logic of which you always protested you had despite the splayed piles of papers, the piles on piles, the very breath of to-do the room held and you exhaled and the papers flew into place via my hands but it was faster than I'd imagined and you didn't diminish with it despite a fiction-prediction but I'm not sure the move won't kill you or that mom's reaction to the move won't kill us both   she worries, repeats phrases, the action like rubbing gose between fingers or sunburned skin peeled and worried between fingertips and sand in an oyster pearl pearl please let it be a pearl and the irritation will be worth it, for the words she says, the same words the same words same order a loop a loop she's knitting knitting her face like a dropped stitch and loop loop, I don't want to sell my house, I don't want to sell, I don't want to sell and it is a forced move but it's not me or dad or anyone but this life which doesn't play by the rules or respect the timetables you have in your head and you've had your share of injustices and they loop, loop in your head, out your lips and it's tiring to listen to   back in August the streets are flooded, the power is out, and the wind explodes drops of rain into horizontal needles which pierce trees which give up their limbs and it's just a moment of extreme force within an ongoing storm   it's an albatross, I yell during the microburst, no electricity, no lights, and the door hits dad's leg and here's the sudden jolt back into illness butted against death as the EMTs come and track rainwater and storm-mud through your house, borrowing a flashlight because the lights are out and they carry him out to the ambulance and we're imprisoned in the dark house together and it's crowded with your worry   this house is a fucking albatross, I repeat and you get angry and it's a Parkinson's anger, different, I can't explain it but I know it, know that it's altered, exaggerated from what has always been here and you're a top that's been spinning just fine for years and then it slows   wobble   wobble   wobble   and I'm watching and you still feel the spinning and it has always worked before and why not now,   why   not   now,   my logic has always worked before, and why   not   now   and   why and why   not   the breaks between the words aren't steady aren't empty they're filled with the gears of your brain getting stuck, jerking

78

forward   I've always   been able   why not   now   because all
has changed and anyone can see it, strangers see it, how we're all in crisis,
how it's a mess, and they see us emergency off-kilter, at risk   the
storm is steady with sure gusts as if his falls don't say it clearly enough:
the first one in February, the broken foot, and then the one in April he
hid, that I'm still not supposed to know about which now seems minor,
and the next one in May, a break as well, a wrist, and then the next
one out of bed in a storm in the August heat and bruised ribs (and
maybe the hip, opening up the landscape to November's hemotoma)
and the next in November which led him to be lying for hours on the
cold floor with infection speed of light speed of poisoned blood through
him, through his heart unable even on a good day to do its job, and the
cold and the bugs in his blood made it thick and the cheering section
was asleep and his heart has its own tenacity and kept on beating, his
body heating up his legs so angry, so angry, and his eyes yellow with
mucus and sometimes he didn't know who I was, who he was, and it's
the worst I've seen him   people see him as a frail old man and so in
the ER when he says he feels worse than when he came in I tell the doc,
the young capable doctor, that dad never complains and they need
to pay attention because he never complains, he never even tells us
things we need to know, although he's getting a bit better and yet the
whole thing is getting more subtle as if running away from his decisions
not to face it and it's running and he can't give chase, he can't on some
days even give a glance and we're playing a game on ice and we're trying
to rub the ice before him to make the surface smooth, fast enough or
slow enough to hit its mark   we're frantic and deep down this
leads to a leaden slowness and when I'm staring into space near
the end of the first week of his hospitalization in November my
mom says that my stare is just like Parkinson's and she laughs and
I don't know her at all and in her head it must be a wild landscape
uniquely hers and confusing and I'm pretty sure a compass wouldn't
work in there because she could convince herself of almost any change
of direction or definition, if it suited her, and she's moving better but
is exhausted with real reason of course and it's too much for all of us
and even at a distance my brother and sister are all torn up, and
mom says, we'll all be devastated when he dies and she's right

                    .
                    .

three days away isn't long or enough and the first night back I'm desperate
for a drink, to lose just a minute, to lose myself for just a minute and I
gulp down the red wine you bought, a thick bordeaux, cold like winter
and warming too, it's this bottle we drink out of tall glasses because we
can't be bothered to handwash the dusty wine glasses   I knock it
back like you see them glug whisky in the movies and it hits me all at once
after dinner at the end of a day when my mom could only be described
as completely batty, affected, exhausted, and no wonder and there's all
these reasons but that doesn't change the fact that I'm at the end of my
tether necessarily, a desired half-cut and me wanting to stop   stop
to not have to handle her, not have to talk smoothly and calmly and
always reasoning when reason has left her, especially today when she's
crazy, loopy, and off subject or always back on that same subject back
and back she's the curl of hair you twist and twist till it pops out, find
it again, twist twist and each time it's too much even when we know
more, even when more is familiar, it's too much and when she doesn't
let up on her loop, when she tells me I've not been there enough I
crack, and then my brother is here and hasn't yet found a way to talk
to her and he snaps too, and is working as hard as he can and it's a
one-way street because she can't see his efforts or that she has to work
too, on many of the same issues, and so it's hitting his head against
a brick wall or sticking his fingers through the weak weave of her
knitting loop loop worry worry and you can't quite tune her out,
it's the pitch of the thing, the ring of truth but it's distorted and
you can't ignore it, white noise, every white noise has its own pitch
you can test it, someone has, and she's the droning of a ceiling fan,
the struggled clicking of the heat when it can't quite turn itself on

lost, new year

This is to say I don't know. Again and again I don't know.

woods shock on waking

Did you know that stress interferes with the working of the hippocampus? Woods shock: all forest, no trees and on my knees I remember nothing. Carrying four people's lives sometimes I sleep on the floor with the baby monitor beside my head. Here I rest for an hour or two, sleeping through my dad's shouts. Help, he says, I'm guessing, clearly, for I'm asleep next door, not quite soundly, but definitely not hearing his voice; it's his shuffle that wakes me, no walker, and his flash of anger, new, and this crush, this rush, this unabated crisis.

Each minute cells convert from normal to not, from place cells which fire in the dark creating maps and easing navigation to anxious cells which press magnetic and so powerful that if you place them too close to anything carrying an electric charge they'll short it.

composite trip to the remnant prairie
cemeteries in central illinois

Up North Avenue we went and then over to St Charles Road and up down, turn around, up down an access road looking for a 'pioneer' cemetery which supposedly lay behind a cement factory, but not so far back as the railroad track. This all used to be prairie, rumor has it, but it's hard to imagine. Concrete desert sprawl and spread and ugly, a stark monstrous ugly over what used to be alive.

The cemetery didn't have prairie as promised because it had been mowed, well planted with 'real' grass, a lawn, and then kept mowed. The stars and stripes flew in the center, barbed wire choked around the top of a new fence, and there was a keep out sign saying you'll be prosecuted to the full extent of the law if you deface or damage anything in the cemetery; the full extent of the law looked expensive with court costs and everything included. Next to the cemetery sat an acre square outlined by an older broken fence which was black with weather (and weather when I don't type the 'w', and before I've typed the 'er', because it's late and my hands are cold reminds me of earth (and will now, always, remind me of earth)) and there was winter prairie here in the second square, looking a bit dead but like it might be alive in the spring and there was snow covered grass on all sides and outside the perimeter grew winter trees with compact birds' nests protected in crooks of branches.

The next prairie was closed for the season.

After that was the one with the DNR truck and the sirens and the power station we didn't see until we were leaving Goose Lake and heading for I-55.

The last stop on our prairie tour took us down a country lane. Snow blown and fenced only by violent barking dogs, we found the cemetery we'd imagined: broken gated, big stoned, with prairie right there among the dead; prickly pear cacti dry and living poking up from snow, and you knew that the settlers knew this prairie as well as the un-prairie trees which had grown because the burning that encouraged prairie, not trees, had stopped, and the lives of the dead were counted in years and months and days if they were much beloved and hadn't lived as long on this earth as the living needed them to make it.

Mom had me bury him in the garden, crown down, flat feet to the sky. We couldn't remember which way to face him, so we faced him towards the house where his attentions should be. It was November, the ground was semi-frozen but it was easy enough to get him in. Over his feet we placed a rock or a paving stone, so we'd remember.

Three months later and his job is done; there are moving vans outside, an ambulance too; men laboring to move my dad, my mom, and I'm in the backyard with my mom who has her finger which she points, there, try there. And I have an ancient dented metal shovel. What I need is a pickax and a treasure map with a big x. I punch the ground and scrape off an inch of icy-dirt. I try to dig deeper, uncover a statue, but my mom's attentions move on.

Over there, honey, try there.

Big boots on stairs. The cop car drives away, the ambulance doors close.

We've got to go, mom.

Alright, but it's supposed to be bad luck to leave him.

The spring will push him up, it'll be fine.

Or the demolition crew will eat the earth. Take the foundations, the oak floors, the faulty wiring, the mice in the walls, the kitchen they built when I was six, the tobacco-stained walls and ceilings, the hidden crawlspaces on the third floor where all of us kids slept at one time or another. The blood, the piss, the shit; the living body which looked dead. Joe has done his job; he'll be released. He'll just have to be patient.

85

crying at dinner

Again. She's crying in public again. Her children visit and take her shopping, bring her grandkids, try to make her laugh, try to improve the things in her life they can improve. There are just so many things no one can change. She wants to change what is, what has passed, sure she does, wouldn't we all like that, but when we don't collude on how everything in the past two years is someone else's fault, how the move is horrible and when we don't say, You're right mom, we forced you to move, she weeps. She is unable to see her own situation clearly (how with Parkinson's she'll need care in the future, every bit as much as dad needs it now) and she cries, almost always in public, or inappropriately when she corners strangers and weeps. They look over her shoulders towards her family, Save me, please.

    Please don't leave me alone in the room with your mother, my girlfriend says.

recovery

I'm writing up a storm. After they move, with a caregiver coming in to help them three days a week, I get a few days, maybe a week, when I don't see them. Then a visit approaches and I have a day of sadness, not dread, before I go up to see them. Sadness when I'm there. Sadness. Then the day with my parents passes in a variety of ways. But the need for recovery the day after is non-negotiable.

731, 7/31

731 has lain empty for months. The grass
waves in the wind; at over two feet long,
it's like prairie grass. If I was a neighbor
I'd think the house had been repossessed.

Mom cries when we go out to dinner.
Fourth time yesterday. She indicated
again how little I'd done for them. Last
night I finally said I'd had enough of her
saying I was abandoning them. I'd had
more than enough. She cried harder.
Told me about her dreams where I leave
and they never see me again.

Dad called this morning to tell me he thought I handled yesterday well. Don't feel any guilt about going back to Scotland, he said. And that stuff about her dream? Absurd. He also said, whether it was intentional or not, it was smart that I was weaning them off me.

731 follows us around after they move. When the family gets together for the 4th of July and has to stay in a motel because, as my mom says, we've sold the house from underneath them, we're put on the 7th floor. The room 731 sits between our rooms and lies empty for the three days.

The day before we move back to Scotland I'm talking to People's Gas, to terminate our service before we leave and the representative says, seemingly out of the blue, Seven Thirty One, right? Excuse me? I ask. In USA-speak our date of departure from the USA is 7/31.

unresolved

All I see is the grief in my dad's eyes in the picture taken in the driveway of 731, when it shows up large as a screensaver. He has tried to shelter me from the sorrow this move has caused.

This difficulty becomes clear in how strong the tears are, how consistent, when I try to re-enter the world of these years and create work from it.

I sort of thought a death would end this. If not end this, define this. But after being taken to that brink again and again, we're still here, confounding expectations, living the unresolved narrative.

between

places

waxwings

We plant pale rowan trees on both
sides of a doorway for protection,
and in winter they stand with bare
spindles for branches, a few hastily
crushed berries on the ground.
Other trees, bigger and nestled
between spruces, are laden. And in
the air, bells.

14 february, morning

If he can walk. If he can support his weight. If he can make it, unaided, to the toilet. If he can remember what it was like to be here, in his house, curious. If only his favorite cereal would taste like it used to. If he could do his taxes. The world is round and the sun wakes him, often colorful before it is bright. There isn't a this or a that, assisted living or skilled nursing. It's a continuum, they say. He slides to the floor, he says. He slides on the slippery floor, twelve times, maybe more. My mom is thin and her rotator cuff causes her problems; she shakes, nearly has blackouts, although she's not fallen yet. He has to sit or lie on the floor until someone else can assist him. This is what we don't want. Weak sun, winter over the lake, which changes daily to ice and to water and back to a state of slush. It undulates especially in the light at dawn. This is morning. The early start so we can make the rounds. I do not set an alarm, I am woken by worries and by this light. I keep the windows wide and wish the air through vents was wind. Even with the window open the world outside and inside is still.

If then this. If all the doctors say his numbers are good, then why is he dying?

If   If   If
                              If
                                        If
                                        If

                              I am woken by worries
and by this light.

     If   If

14 february, nighttime

We start this day with a conversation, talking about how he could walk out of rehab. This is where we end the day: 2mg of morphine, his dry lips, his closed eyes, until they are open and he asks what day it is and I tell him, it's valentine's day, the 14th of February. Today is Sunday. Tomorrow is Monday the 15th. He closes his eyes. Sleeps. Maybe. Or drifts between places. A soft press of my hand to his chest, his bulky rib cage. This is to say I don't know. And I do. I am lost. Again and again I don't know what to do in the minute, to move us out of that minute and successfully into the next one.

After talking about rehab I say it, raise it, that maybe there is another way. I'm not sure. He is; he's sure. That's what I want, he says. He is sure. The pain in his hands, his legs. He wants to go peacefully, quietly. I hope we can manage that. Back at their apartment my three-year-old neice puts hearts on us, peeled from a sheet of stickers, and her sixteen-month-old sister: her red cheeks, her grin as we run the halls.

I work; it is a relief to simply teach. We have parameters for what we focus on, what needs to be said. Writing is a place I can be silent, in that I don't have to speak. There is relief in that. This is not my normal way.

I am silent with those I love, and maybe with those I can't be bothered to fight or negotiate with. I am not worried and I don't explain. They may be worried, they may want to demand explanation. Here, in this Italian café, I am quiet and I don't have to say anything but, A black coffee and a glass of water, please.

As my brother wrote in the obituary, my dad took his own counsel. His thought processes, when we were young, were never exposed. As he got older, old, things just didn't work as he needed them to, like his hands, in particular, and later his hands and his legs and his brain, and that sharpness by which he always defined himself was lost. And if he couldn't do it to the standard he'd always done it, he couldn't do it at all. Three years of taxes, and a re-drafted will, two years old, both left incomplete, unsigned. My dad, I'm thinking, in some things, had no between places when it came to his own expectations of himself.

Luckily for me he did have these places for those he loved. And like the best readers of fiction, the witnesses of art, or the best audience members, he met us at that place, asked questions, and kept coming back, so he'd be comfortable between tides; between gay and straight; between loving and questioning.

This is the space where we met again and again in our talks: at the top of the hill, between arguments, in complicated heightened places. And so it makes sense that at the end he'd take me to somewhere like this.

In the last few years, in times of occasional and acute illness, it has sometimes felt as if my dad was existing between places, here and the future, between life and death. Littoral, ecotone, twilight.

Dying is another between place, and is, for me, the most recently added. When somebody prepares to die they are a bit in both worlds. Life is here, loosening its hold, and death and after death are before us. For some this is an open space not defined by a single or simple idea and I think that's the way dying was for my dad.

On Sunday the 14th of February dad chose to go into Hospice; he spoke his wishes and reasons clearly and compassionately. On Monday the 15th he nearly died at midday, and then he dreamt he'd died during Monday night. When he woke up on Tuesday, still alive, he was a bit baffled, I'd even say a bit disappointed, and he couldn't understand why he was still here. But what he did say over and over is that where he had been had been great.

Sometimes we honor by living and by doing. Sometimes a simple action, the simplicity of taking action, is something that releases the brakes on the rails, and becomes a type of flying, a joy in speed. My sixteen-month-old niece knows this. When you hold her and run with her she trusts you have her, she trusts you to hold her, and to give her a thrill, and she allows the air to push her back, to rough her up. Her face is brilliantly lit. It could be you or someone else who holds her and runs with her but what matters is that she is carried and she trusts you and she lets go.

In his last week, dad talked about the cartoon Calvin and Hobbes, specifically he described the last comic strip Bill Watterson drew of the duo back in December 2005. They're at the top of a snowy hill, Hobbes carrying the sled. It's a magical world, Hobbes 'ol buddy, says Calvin, and after years of adventures they simply hop on the sled and speed down the hill, Let's go exploring.

This is how some choose to travel from one place to another.

how she travels

we draw a line

between what we have been and who we want
to become. My sister and I are instantly lighter.
So are our phone conversations. When mom
has been in the hospital and is in rehab, again,
and when a new diagnosis is found scribbled in
her medical notes, confirmed in conversations,
we talk about what we know: mom is going to
have to move, again.

    I'll play bad cop, my sister says.

    I'll book my tickets. I'll be bad cop
next time.

    Deal.

hallucinations

She sees chickens pecking in the grass across this suburban street, where there is an apartment building made of brick and in the sky above this building she sees a train, the same time every day. Can you hear it?

Middle-of-the-night revelers call out to her and she, who can barely walk, gets out of bed, spins open the window and sees a procession of people in long, heavy robes – chanting – and then, back in bed, wildly tossed by sleep, she raises her arms to the sky and says his name, the name of this man who had troubled her so when he was alive.

When she chokes, we lift her arms to open a pathway and sometimes we call in Heimlich to help her out.

Multiple seizures, the email reads, and we wake up one morning, in Padova, Italy, in our room facing the basilica; we wake with sunlight making a bright cross on the wall through half-closed curtains and it's brightest at the center, where the two arms meet, bright as the bald sun above a summer desert at noon.

multiple system atrophy, parkinson's meaner cousin

She's all absence, fingers long and thin like a bird skeleton, with her nails painted dark blue, a treat. Her touch lacks subtlety and raises in me a muscle memory of being tickled when I was a kid, those long fingers, sharp digging nails, and now veins and tendons push up through skin as she reaches out to the grandkids and pulls a child towards her narrow impossible body which is so easily hidden behind a four-year-old.

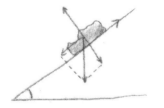

sing

She could never sing as well as she thought she could and for years we'd always complain and request that she stop singing. But then in this last year we will do anything, as her kids, to take her out of her body and bring her to joy for this minute, for this minute, for this. We put on Kenny Rogers, Joan Baez, Johnny Cash and we join her in the singing. Because it takes her out of her dying body and because when sitting she can't swallow but she can sing, we sing.

cantors

In the alien landscape outside her apartment roots arch out from trees like ribs, and mom is so thin, so very thin in this final year. I ache to curve myself into the space between her intolerant nostalgia and my own intolerant living grief and while her fragile lap cannot take my weight, her arms make the attempt to hold me. There is a solidness to the hard edge of her cheek and the clarity of her voice as she sings, and the sounds she makes are laughter and joy and occasional sorrow.

I am my own beast with ears attuned to better hear the cries of those who are gone and those who are passing through what is known and entering into the bigger world of what is unseen.

In brief seconds as I take one step, maybe two, away from her, the approach of her hooded cantors can be heard. She is something else without us, and what we do not know of the people we love is that they dance naked but for this mask or that mask or for sorrow that sings like a siren and is carried impossible distances. We do not know if those lips are about to move in a choke or thanks or death and what she sees is not what I see and what it means to me is not what is intended and is not what it means to you.

①

Thursday 18th
am

12:30 Haloperdol
1:30   Haloperdol
2:30   Haloperdol + Atropine
3:30   Haloperdol + Hydromorphine
4:30   Hydromorphine
6:00   Lorazepam
6:30   Atropine
7:15   Haloperdol + Hydromorphine
9:00   Haloperdol + Hydromorphine
12:30 Haloperdol + Hydromorphine
1:30   Ativan (0.5) Hydromorphine (0.5ml)
3:30   Ativan (0.5) Hydromorphine (.25ml)
5:30   Lorazepam / Hydromorphone
7:30   Lorazepam / Hydromorphone
9:30 - Lorazepam / Hydramorphine
11:30 Lorazepam / Hydromorphone (.25ml)
       Friday 19th am   ↳ Towards Window
1:30   Haloperdol -
Towards
Bathroom
3:30   Haloperdol / Lorazepam
towards
Window

5:30 Lorazepam/Hyrdomorphone
7:30 Lorazepam/Hyrdomorphone
9:30 Lorazepam/Hyrdomorphone
11:30 Lorazepam/Hydromorphon
12:30pm Lorazepam ———
1:00pm ——— Hydromorphone
                       Mauth stuff

1:30 haldol
7:00 Lorazepam/Hydromorphone
9:15 Lorazepam/Hydromorphone
11:10 Lorazepam/Hydromorphone
1:10am Lorazepam/Hydromorphone   (Sat)
3:10 Lorazepam/Hydromorphone
5:10 Lorazepam/Hydromorphone
7:10 Lorazepam/Hydromorphone
9:10 Lorazepam/Hydromorphone
11:05 Lorazepam/Hydromorphone
1:00pm Haldol
1:15pm Lorazepam/Hydromorphone
4:10 — Lorazepam/Hydromorphone
6:30 — Lorazepam/Hydromorphone
7:30 Haldol/Atropine/hydromorphone
6:30 hydromorphone

how she travels

For a long time, my mom denied travel would be a part of this. She denied things she did not like, which were out of her control: her dizziness, her falls, her difficulty swallowing, her need to sleep all day and night, her inability to finally be free and independent.

Fifteen months before she dies, before she has caregivers, we fail mom. We fail to keep her safe and more than once she is all bruises and black-eyes from dramatic falls, which aren't really falls, but rather they're like a force comes and propels her through the air. That's what she says once, when she gets stuck between a piece of furniture and the wall. Even then she is disorientated and furious she's in the hospital, furious she's in rehab, and she's still unable to carry full conversations through. The process of coming to understand is brutal. Her new diagnosis, Multiple System Atrophy, is a death warrant but she can't grasp it.

In the spring, after more falls, greater weight loss, a gasp of pneumonia, we bring in Hospice. They talk to her, regularly, and she starts to understand and we see the difference: she's clearer, sometimes, and knows in this hour or that day that her diagnosis has changed from something she can live with to something that will kill her. Her need to protect her children is so great that even though we've been the ones trying to make her life a good one within a siege of illness, she, somewhere, thinks that she's protected us from the truth and that we don't know she's dying. She believes we will be shocked.

We are shocked. How the weight drops off her. How the falls continue. How the choking worsens.

learned

Over the phone I heard
mom's favorite music
playing. She's agitated,
my sister said.

I remember how silent
I finally learned to be
in dad's room. Maybe
turn off the music, I said.

Sat

10:45 pm hydromorphone

11:30 pm hydromorphone
midnight Atropine/lorazipan
2:00 hydromorphone/lorazepam

Acknowledgements

'thundersnow', 'dnr', 'baseball-hail' and 'composite trip to
the remnant pioneer prairie cemeteries in central illinois'
appeared in *PN Review* 178, 2008.

'summer', 'as we migrate', 'driving back to the apartment' ('lsd'),
'the healthy one' and 'buildings define' appeared in *Cleave:
New Writings by Women in Scotland*, 2008.

'witness, dual national' was published in the Books Section of
The Herald on Saturday, 3 November 2007.

elements of 'between places & 'this year' appeared in *PN Review*
196, November 2010, as the essay 'between places: if then
essay'.

versions of 'hallucinations' and 'MSA' appeared in *Lighthouse
Literary Journal*, November 2013.

'what we did not know', 'lost wax casting' and 'ghosts' appeared
in *New Writing Dundee*, 2015.

An Tobar, on the Isle of Mull, commissioned a creative/critical
response to their Zembla exhibition on imagined lands.

'Cantor' is a fugitive version of a longer essay written for this.

'microburst' appeared in *Lune* 01, April 2018 and in
PROTOTYPE 2, July 2020.

Notes and Influences

It is sheer good fortune to miss somebody before they leave you.
  Toni Morrison, *Sula*. Penguin Books, New York: 1982 [1973]

p.25
my memories – those elusive, fragmentary patches of color...
  Annie Dillard, 'To Fashion a Text' in *Inventing the Truth:*
  The Art and Craft of Memoir, William Zinsser (ed.). First
  Mariner Books, New York: 1998 [1987]

p.33
Lost really has two disparate meanings... moments of discovery.
  Rebecca Solnit, *A Field Guide to Getting Lost.* Canongate,
  Edinburgh: 2006

p.52
The great salt lake... an extensive change in shoreline.
  Rebecca Solnit, *A Field Guide to Getting Lost.*

p.55
These parables say... it's awareness of knowledge's limits.
  Rebecca Solnit, *A Field Guide to Getting Lost.*

p.59
The view here is truly magnificent... we now made a kind of tea from
the roots of the wild cherry tree.
  John C Fremont, *Narratives of Exploration and Adventure*,
  Alan Nevins (ed.) Longmans, Green & Co., London: 1956
  [1845]

p.75
jungle fear comes from 'On Sylvia Plath' a short talk by
  Anne Carson in *Plainwater*. First Vintage Contemporaries
  Edition: 2000

( ) (   ) p   prototype
poetry / prose / interdisciplinary projects /
anthologies

Creating new possibilities in the publishing of fiction and
poetry through a flexible, interdisciplinary approach and the
production of unique and beautiful books.

Prototype is an independent publisher working across genres
and disciplines, committed to discovering and sharing work that
exists outside the mainstream.
    Each publication is unique in its form and presentation,
and the aesthetic of each object is considered critical to its
production.
    Prototype strives to increase audiences for experimental
writing, as the home for writers and artists whose work requires
a creative vision not offered by mainstream literary publishers.

In its current, evolving form, Prototype consists of 4 strands
of publications:
    (type 1 – poetry)
    (type 2 – prose)
    (type 3 – interdisciplinary projects)
    (type 4 – anthologies) including an annual
    anthology of new work, *PROTOTYPE*.

microbursts
Elizabeth Reeder & Amanda Thomson
Published by Prototype in 2021

Text by Elizabeth Reeder
The structure of the collection is a collaboration
between Reeder and Thomson
Images, artwork and original format by Amanda Thomson
Typeset in Plantin by Traven T. Croves
Printed in xxxx by xxxx

isbn 978-1-913513-06-1

( )   (   )   p   prototype

(type 3 – interdisciplinary projects)
www.prototypepublishing.co.uk
@prototypepubs

prototype publishing
71 oriel road
london e9 5sg
uk